*The purpose of life, after all, is to live it, to taste experience to the utmost,
to reach out eagerly and without fear for newer and richer experience.*

—ELEANOR ROOSEVELT (1884–1962)
American stateswoman

a woman's notebook III
Being a blank book
with quotes by women

We don't see things as they are, we see them as we are.

— ANAIS NIN (1903–1977)
American diarist and writer

The really frightening thing about middle age is the knowledge that you'll outgrow it.

—DORIS DAY, b. 1924
American actress

Life is what happens to you when you're making other plans.

—BETTY TALMADGE, b. 1924
American meat broker

Rose-colored glasses are never made in bifocals. Nobody wants to read the small print in dreams.

—ANN LANDERS, b. 1918
American newspaper columnist

I don't believe man is woman's natural enemy. Perhaps his lawyer is.

— SHANA ALEXANDER, b. 1925
American journalist

A man's home may seem to be his castle on the outside; inside it is more often his nursery.

—CLARE BOOTH LUCE (1903–1987)
American ambassador and writer

Sometimes I wonder if men and women really suit each other. Perhaps they should live next door and just visit now and then.

—KATHERINE HEPBURN, b. 1909
American actress

I live by a man's code, designed to fit a man's world, yet at the same time I never forget that a woman's first job is to choose the right shade of lipstick.

—CAROLE LOMBARD (1908-1942)
American actress

according to you or
" " the men?
I THINK NOT!

Self-pity in its early stages is as snug as a feather mattress. Only when it hardens does it become uncomfortable.

—MAYA ANGELOU, b. 1928
American writer

A woman can look both moral and exciting—if she also looks as if it was quite a struggle.

—EDNA FERBER (1887–1968)
American novelist

Always there remains portions of our heart into which no one is able to enter, invite them as we may.

—MARY DIXON THAYER (Twentieth Century)
American writer

My soul never thinks of beginning to wake up for other people till lunch-time, and never does so completely till it has been taken out of doors and aired in the sunshine. Who can begin conventional amiability the first thing in the morning? It is the hour of savage instincts and natural tendencies.

—COUNTESS VAN ARNIM (1866–1941)
English writer

Why not be oneself? That is the whole secret of a successful appearance. If one is a greyhound, why try to look like a Pekingese?

—EDITH SITWELL (1887–1964)
English writer

Woman's discontent increases in exact proportion to her development.

—ELIZABETH CADY STANTON (1815–1902)
American suffragist

Marrying a man is like buying something you've been admiring for a long time in a shop window. You may love it when you get home, but it doesn't always go with everything else in the house.

—JEAN KERR, b. 1923
American humorist

Personally I think if a woman hasn't met the right man by the time she is 24, she may be lucky.

—DEBORAH KERR, b. 1921
Scottish actress

In real life, I assure you, there is no such thing as algebra.

—FRAN LEBOWITZ, b. 1950
American humorist

A mother is neither cocky, nor proud, because she knows the school principal may call at any minute to report that her child had just driven a motorcycle through the gymnasium.

—MARY KAY BLAKELY b. 1957
American writer

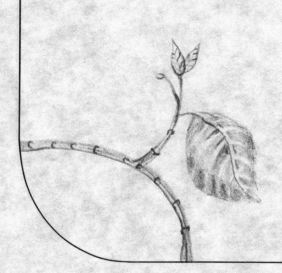

A man has to be Joe McCarthy to be called ruthless. All a woman has to do is put you on hold.

—MARLO THOMAS, b. 1943
American actress

When a man gets up to speak, people listen, then look. When a woman gets up, people look; then, if they like what they see, they listen.

—PAULINE FREDERICK (1883–1938)
American actress

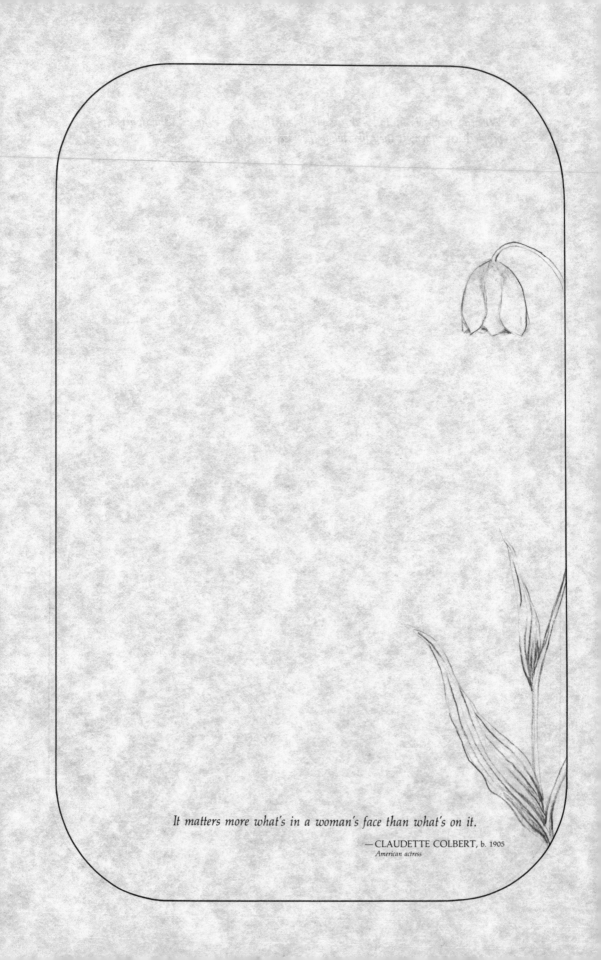

It matters more what's in a woman's face than what's on it.

—CLAUDETTE COLBERT, b. 1905
American actress

I may not be a lioness, but I am a lion's cub.

Trouble is a part of your life, and if you don't share it, you don't give the person who loves you enough chance to love you enough.

—DINAH SHORE, b. 1917
American entertainer

Selfishness is not living as one wishes to live, it is asking others to live as one wishes to live.

—RUTH RENDELL, b. 1930
English mystery novelist

Sensuality is complicated. Love is intricate. And the flesh is sweet, but I no longer mistake it for the whole thing.

—CHRIS CHASE (Twentieth Century)
American writer

Chains do not hold a marriage together. It is threads, hundreds of tiny threads, which sew people together through the years.

—SIMONE SIGNORET (1921-1985)
French actress

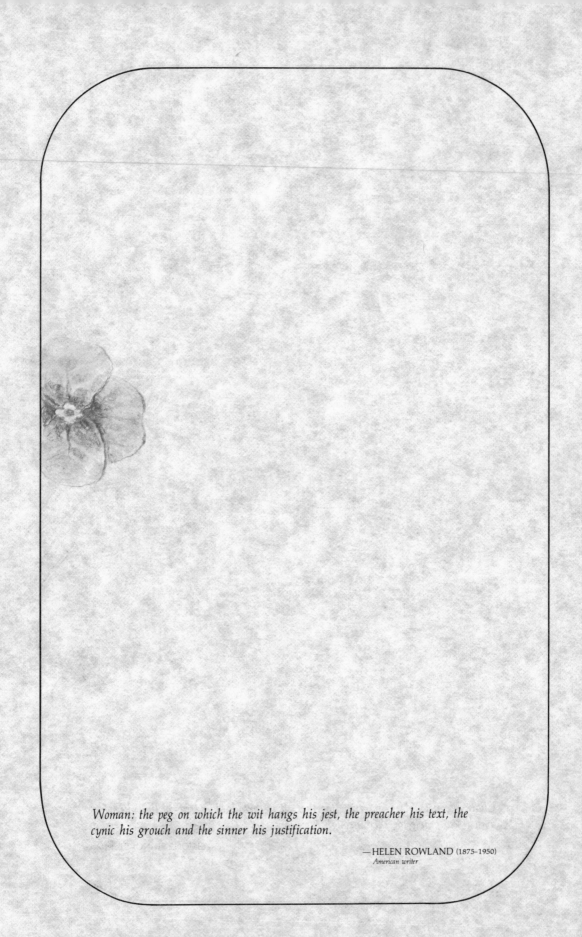

Woman: the peg on which the wit hangs his jest, the preacher his text, the cynic his grouch and the sinner his justification.

—HELEN ROWLAND (1875–1950)
American writer

Cleaning your house while your kids are still growing is like shoveling the walk before it stops snowing.

—PHYLLIS DILLER, b. 1917
American humorist

No woman should be shamefaced in attempting through her work, to give back to the world a portion of its lost heart.

—LOUISE BOGAN (1897–1970)
American poet

Men are taught to apologize for their weaknesses, women for their strengths.

—LOIS WYSE, b. 1926
American advertising executive

What is it I got that makes them twitch?

—MARILYN MONROE, (1926–1962)
American actress

Brevity is the soul of lingerie.

—DOROTHY PARKER (1893–1967)
American writer

Not all women give most of their waking thoughts to pleasing men. Some are married.

—EMMA LEE (Twentieth Century)
American writer

God gave us our relatives; thank God we can choose our friends.

— ETHEL WATTS MUMFORD (1878–1940)
American writer

I learned long ago that being Lewis Carroll was infinitely more exciting than being Alice.

—JOYCE CAROL OATES, b. 1938
American writer

If love is the answer, could you please rephrase the question?

—LILY TOMLIN, b. 1939
American comedienne

All women are said to believe that the imported male is always more desirable than the domestic.

— ALICE McDERMOTT, b. 1953
American writer

Of two evils choose the prettier.

—CAROLYN WELLS (1870–1942)
American writer

When men talk about defense, they always claim to be protecting women and children, but they never ask the women and children what they think.

—PAT SCHROEDER, b. 1940
American Congresswoman

The only thing that seems eternal and natural in motherhood is ambivalence.

—JANE LAZARRE, b. 1943
American writer

*My husband and I have figured out a really good system
about the housework: neither one of us does it.*

—DOTTIE ARCHIBALD (Twentieth Century)
American writer

Bigamy is having one husband too many. Monogamy is the same.

ANONYMOUS PROVERB

Why is it that the man who takes perfectly good care of himself when there is no female in his life becomes helpless around the house when he starts sharing it with a woman?

—BETTE-JANE RAPHAEL (Twentieth Century)
American writer

I don't know how long I like my egg boiled, but it's exactly right by the time I've finished my hair.

—BETTY FURNESS, b. 1916
American stateswoman

And then, not expecting it, you become middle-aged and anonymous. No one notices you. You achieve a wonderful freedom. It is a positive thing. You can move about, unnoticed and invisible.

—DORIS LESSING, b. 1919
English writer

The post office has a great charm at one period of our lives. When you have lived to my age, you will begin to think letters are never worth going through the rain for.

—JANE AUSTEN (1775–1815)
English novelist

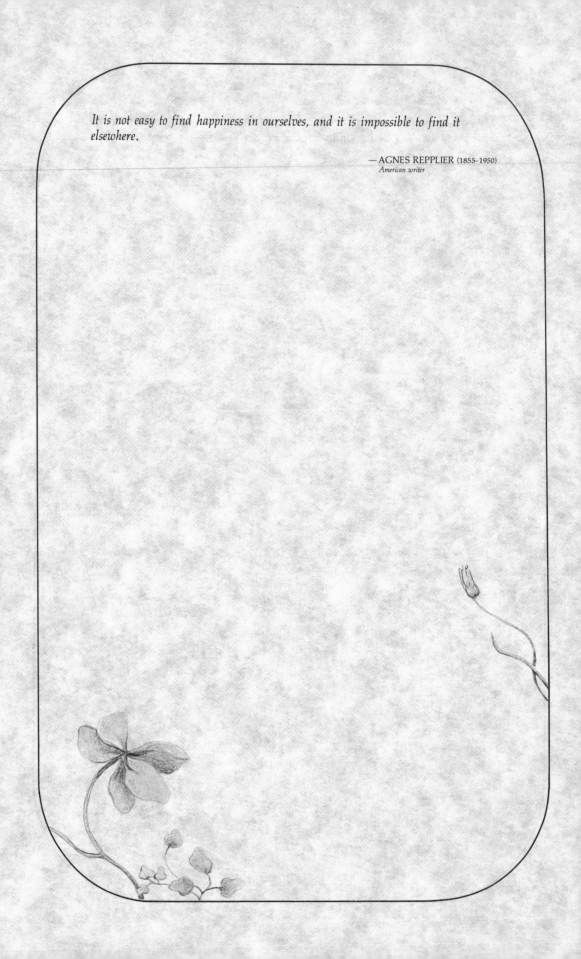

It is not easy to find happiness in ourselves, and it is impossible to find it elsewhere.

— AGNES REPPLIER (1855–1950)
American writer

Laugh, and the world laughs with you;
Weep, and you weep alone;
For the sad old earth must borrow its mirth,
But has trouble enough of its own.

—ELLA WHEELER WILCOX (1850–1919)
American poet and journalist

I do want to get rich but I never want to do what there is to do to get rich.

—GERTRUDE STEIN (1874–1946)
American writer

People who fight fire with fire usually end up with ashes.

— ABIGAIL VAN BUREN, b. 1918
American newspaper columnist

I buy clothes made for men, every one of whom intends, according to a curiously outdated conviction among clothing manufacturers, to wear his clothes for decades.

—INGEBORG DAY, b. 1941
Swedish writer

Age is something that doesn't matter, unless you are a cheese.

—BILLIE BURKE (1886–1970)
American actress

I prefer the word "homemaker" because "housewife" always implies that there may be a wife someplace else.

—BELLA ABZUG, b. 1920
American politician

I feel about airplanes the way I feel about diets. It seems to me that they are wonderful things for other people to go on.

—JEAN KERR, b. 1923
American humorist

When she raises her eyelids, it's as if she were taking off all her clothes.

—COLETTE (1873–1953)
French novelist

Love ceases to be a pleasure when it ceases to be a secret.

— APHRA BEHN (1640-1689)
English writer

The only adults I know who are marching along their one true course are boring, insensitive or lucky.

—ELLEN GOODMAN, b. 1941
American columnist

If you take a woman fishing, she has to be a dull one. Anybody lively scares away the fish.

—ELIZABETH JENKINS, b. 1905
English writer

To live is so startling it leaves little time for anything else.

—EMILY DICKINSON (1830–1886)
American poet

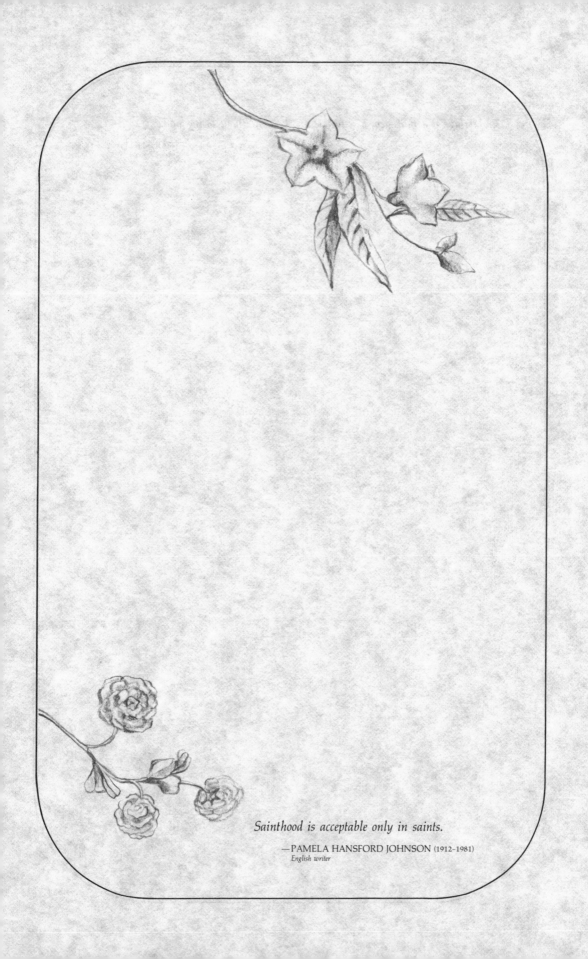

Sainthood is acceptable only in saints.

—PAMELA HANSFORD JOHNSON (1912–1981)
English writer

Marriage is a half step, a way to leave home without losing home.

—GAIL SHEEHY, b. 1937
American writer

Someday perhaps change will occur when times are ready for it instead of always when it is too late. Someday change will be accepted as life itself.

—SHIRLEY MACLAINE, b. 1934
American actress

I do not think that I could ever really love a woman who had not, at one time or another, been up on a broomstick.

—ISAK DINESEN (1885–1962)
Danish writer

How hard it is to escape from places! However carefully one goes, they hold you — you leave little bits of yourself fluttering on the fences, little rags and shreds of your very life.

—KATHERINE MANSFIELD (1888–1923)
New Zealand writer

The most popular labor-saving device is still money.

—PHYLLIS GEORGE, b. 1949
American sports broadcaster

Glamour is what makes a man ask for your telephone number. But it also is what makes a woman ask for the name of your dressmaker.

—LILY DACHE, b. 1901
American designer

Boyfriends weren't friends at all; they were prizes, escorts, symbols of achievement, fascinating strangers, the Other.

—SUSAN ALLEN TOTH, b. 1940
American writer

To fall in love is awfully simple, but to fall out of love is simply awful.

—BESS MYERSON, b. 1924
American columnist

A diamond is the only kind of ice that keeps a girl warm.

—ELIZABETH TAYLOR, b. 1932
American actress

A gossip is one who talks to you about others; a bore is one who talks to you about himself; and a brilliant conversationalist is one who talks to you about yourself.

—LISA KIRK, b. 1925
American actress

Thinking about my husband's retirement, I realized I married him for better or for worse—not for lunch.

—JANE COOKMAN, b. 1924
American homemaker

The hardest task in a girl's life is to prove to a man that his intentions are serious.

—HELEN ROWLAND (1875–1950)
American journalist

If it's very painful for you to criticize your friends — you're safe in doing it.
But if you take the slightest pleasure in it, that's the time to hold your tongue.

—ALICE DUER MILLER (1874–1942)
American poet

Whenever I dwell for any length of time on my own shortcomings, they gradually begin to seem mild, harmless, rather engaging little things, not at all like the staring defects in other people's characters.

—MARGARET HALSEY, b. 1910
American writer

The years a woman subtracts from her age are never lost; they are added to the ages of other women.

—DIANE DE POITIERS (1499–1566)
Duchesse de Velentois

Every time I think that I'm getting old, and gradually going to the grave, something else happens.

—LILLIAN CARTER (1898–1983)
American humanitarian

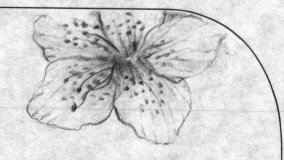

I know a lot of people didn't expect our relationship to last—but we've just celebrated our two months' anniversary.

—BRITT EKLAND, b. 1944
Scandanavian actress

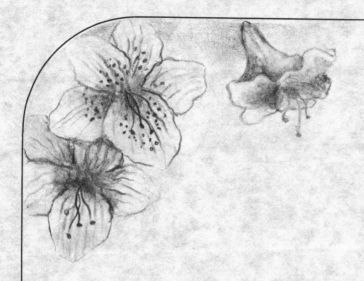

Our strength is often composed of the weakness we're damned if we're going to show.

—MIGNON MCLAUGHLIN (Twentieth Century)
American writer

Everything else you grow out of, but you never recover from childhood.

—BERYL BAINBRIDGE, b. 1933
American writer

Lovers, children, heroes, none of them do we fantasize as extravagantly as we fantasize our parents.

—FRANCINE DU PLESSIX GRAY, b. 1930
French-born American writer

When he is late for dinner and I know he must be either having an affair or lying dead in the street, I always hope he's dead.

—JUDITH VIORST, b. 1931
American poet

Life itself is the proper binge.

—JULIA CHILD, b. 1912
American chef

What a lovely surprise to finally discover how unlonely being alone can be.

—ELLEN BURSTYN, b. 1932
American actress